THE OFFICIAL AIR BRAKE HANDBOOK

This handbook is only a guide. For official purposes, please refer to the Ontario Highway Traffic Act and regulations. This handbook should not be used as a guide for repairs, which should only be carried out by a qualified person.

To request a copy of this book in an alternate format, contact Publications Ontario at 1-800-668-9938 or (416) 326-5300 or visit www.publications.gov.on.ca.

Disponible en français
Demandez le « Guide officiel de l'utilisation des freins à air »

Driving is a privilege — not a right

1

Introduction

In Ontario, most large commercial vehicles are equipped with an air brake system. You must have an air brake endorsement on your driver's licence to drive these vehicles.

The purpose of this handbook is to introduce you to the knowledge and skills you need to drive a vehicle with air brakes in a safe and lawful manner. It contains the information you need to prepare for the air brake endorsement examination. Air Brake examinations are conducted at DriveTest Centres.

As you read this handbook, remember it is only a guide. It contains basic information about common air brake systems. Each vehicle and its air brake system may have features and components that are different from those described in this handbook. As a driver, it is your responsibility to become familiar with all the characteristics of a vehicle before you drive it.

CONTENTS

4

If you are driving a vehicle equipped with air brakes, it is important to understand how an air brake system works and how it compares to other vehicle braking systems. This chapter outlines the fundamentals of the most common braking systems used in vehicles today.

Stopping a vehicle

A moving vehicle is a form of energy. The energy comes from the fuel that is burned by the vehicle's engine. To stop a moving vehicle, its energy must be changed into another form by the brake system.

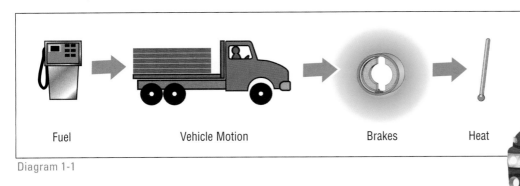

| Fuel | Vehicle Motion | Brakes | Heat |

Diagram 1-1

Brakes convert the energy of a moving vehicle (mechanical energy) into heat energy by developing friction between fixed and moving brake parts. Friction is the force that resists movement between two surfaces in contact with each other. Friction produces heat. When you press the brake pedal in a moving vehicle, you are causing a surface that is not moving with the wheel (the brake shoe linings or pads) to move against a surface that is revolving with the wheel (the brake drums or discs). The harder the pressure, the more the mechanical energy is converted to heat energy, and the quicker the wheels slow down. The amount of energy that must be converted into heat by the brake system depends upon the size, speed and weight of the vehicle.

Air brakes differ from hydraulic brakes

Most brakes are located at the wheels of a vehicle. The force you apply to the brake pedal is transmitted to the wheels to make the brakes operate. There are two main ways in which this force is transmitted — hydraulic brake systems and air brake systems.

Hydraulic brake systems are used as the main braking system on almost all passenger vehicles and light trucks. Hydraulic brakes use brake fluid to transmit force when the brakes are applied. Since brake fluid cannot be compressed, force is transmitted immediately and directly at each wheel when you press the brake pedal.

Air brake systems are used on large commercial vehicles because they can develop and transmit high mechanical forces over great distances using simple components

and connections. Air brake systems use compressed air, which is stored in tanks, to produce the force that applies the brakes at each wheel.

When you press the brake pedal, compressed air must travel from one part of the system to another. Special valves make sure that the air moves through the system as quickly as possible; however, there is a split-second delay in brake reaction from the moment you apply or release the brake pedal.

This split-second delay in brake reaction occurs in all air brake systems.

Components of air brakes

All vehicles using air brake systems have one of two major brake types at the wheels — drum brakes or disc brakes. You must be able to recognize the brake hardware — also called foundation brake components — used at the wheels of your vehicle.

Drum brakes use a drum with brake shoes and linings inside the drum. When you press the brake pedal, the brake shoes press outward against the drum's surface.

Disc brakes use a disc-shaped rotor and a caliper containing brake pads. When you press the brake pedal, the pads press toward each other, clamping against both sides of the rotor's surface.

You can find more information about foundation brake components in Chapter 6.

Other braking systems

Along with hydraulic and air brake systems, there are a number of other kinds of braking systems used in vehicles. For example:

- **Air-over-hydraulic brakes** are used mainly on medium-duty commercial vehicles. This system uses compressed air in combination with a hydraulic brake system. (You must have an air brake endorsement on your driver's licence to drive a vehicle with air-over-hydraulic brakes in Ontario.)
- **Air parking brakes** are used on some medium duty vehicles such as school buses. This system provides an air-operated parking brake and a hydraulic brake system for all other braking. (You do not need an air brake endorsement on your driver's licence to drive a vehicle with air parking brakes.)

Key Points To Remember
- Brakes convert the energy of a moving vehicle into heat.
- Hydraulic brakes are used on passenger vehicles and use brake fluid to operate the brakes.
- Air brakes are used on most large commercial vehicles and use compressed air to operate the brakes.
- A split-second delay in brake reaction is present in all air brake systems.
- Vehicles with air brakes may use either drum or disc type components.

Chapter 2

AIR SUPPLY SUBSYSTEM

Air brake systems are made up of several subsystems. This chapter explains the operation and function of the air supply subsystem, which produces, stores and manages the compressed air used by the brake system.

Note: There is a circuit diagram of the air supply subsystem on page 81.

Air compressor

An air compressor produces air for the brake system. Powered by the vehicle's engine, the air compressor draws in air at normal pressure and forces it into a much smaller space, causing the pressure of the air to increase. This compressed air is a form of stored energy.

Air pressure is usually measured in kiloPascals (kPa) or pounds per square inch (psi). The normal range of air pressure in an air brake system is between 552 and 932 kPa (80 and 135 psi).

Air compressors are generally powered directly by the vehicle's engine or by using belts and pulleys and can be mounted either directly on the engine or by brackets and fasteners. The brackets and fasteners must be kept secure so that the air compressor can work properly. All components used to attach and power the air compressor must be kept in good condition to ensure a constant supply of compressed air.

Diagram 2-1: **Air compressor**

Governor

Air compressors are designed to run whenever the engine is running. As a result, they are able to produce much more air than is needed by the brake system. To prevent the compressor from producing too much compressed air and to reduce the load on the engine, a governor is used in the air brake system. When air pressure is high enough in the system, the governor causes the compressor to stop pumping air (cut-out). When the air pressure drops to a certain point, the governor will cause the compressor to start pumping air again (cut-in).

Diagram 2-2: Governor

Normal pressure range

The points where the air compressor is turned on and off determine the normal operating pressure range of an air brake system. Cut-out pressure normally ranges from 828 to 932 kPa (120 to 135 psi). Cut-in pressure is normally 138 to 173 kPa (20 to 25 psi) below the cut-out setting and must never be less than 552 kPa (80 psi). The minimum

Diagram 2-3: Pressure gauge (Outer green band shows normal range.)

and maximum pressure settings prescribed in the Ontario Highway Traffic Act and regulations are 552 kPa (80 psi) and 932 kPa (135 psi).

Important: A vehicle should only be driven when air pressure is in the normal operating range. A drop in air pressure below the normal cut-in setting is a sign that the air brake system is malfunctioning or that an abnormal demand is being placed on the system. Bring the vehicle to a safe stop as soon as possible. Proceed only when air pressure returns to its normal operating range and all other air brake system functions are normal.

Air tanks

Air from the compressor is stored in air tanks. Located under or around the frame of the vehicle, these tanks are usually made of steel and shaped like cylinders with domed ends. Vehicles may use one, two, three or more tanks depending on the specific needs of the vehicle. In some cases,

two tanks are housed within one cylinder using an internal separator that is not visible from the outside.

The air that is drawn in by the air compressor contains moisture or humidity. As the air is compressed and passed into the tanks, the moisture condenses or 'drops out' of the air and settles to the bottom of the tank. Oil used to lubricate the air compressor may also mix with the air that passes through the compressor and settle at the bottom of the tank.

Supply or 'wet' tank

The first tank that the compressed air enters is called the supply tank. Since it collects most of the moisture and oil that drops out of the air, it is also called a 'wet' tank. If the mixture of moisture and oil that collects in the supply tank passes into the rest of the air brake system, it can damage brake components and interfere with the operation of the system. The following are some of the problems that can occur.

- The collected moisture and oil mixture can form a sludge that can pass from the tank into other components of the air brake system, damaging seals and causing brake valves to stick.
- The mixture of moisture and oil can become corrosive and damage the air tank and other system components.
- Moisture in the brake system can freeze in cold temperatures and may cause brake failure.
- Too much moisture and oil collecting in the air tanks can reduce the volume of air and may cause brake failure.

Air tank drain valve

Moisture and oil must be drained from the tanks on a regular basis. Many vehicle manufacturers recommend that the vehicle's air tanks be drained daily. This is

Diagram 2-4

done through the air tank drain valve, located at the bottom of each air tank. Remember to check each tank to be sure it is fully drained and watch for anything abnormal about the discharge from the tank.

One-way check valve

When air flows out of the supply tank, it is prevented from returning by one-way check valves. When

draining the tanks, the supply tank should always be drained first to prevent accumulated moisture from the supply tank flowing into the next tank being drained. When the supply tank is drained first, any accumulated moisture is removed before it can pass further into the system.

Remember: Always drain the supply tank first.

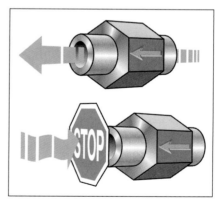

Diagram 2-5: **One-way check valve**

Dual service (primary and secondary) tanks

When air leaves the supply tank, it splits into two circuits, passing into primary and secondary air tanks called dual service tanks. These are also called 'dry' tanks because they collect less moisture than the supply or 'wet' tank. Having two delivery circuits is a safety feature that ensures if one circuit fails, the other circuit will provide enough brake function to stop the vehicle. The two circuits are referred to as the primary circuit and the secondary circuit.

Air dryer

Vehicles may use an air dryer to reduce the amount of moisture that passes into the air brake system. An air dryer is located between the air compressor and the supply tank. Air that is pumped by the air compressor passes through the air dryer where it cools and passes through a drying material. This removes moisture from the air before it enters the supply tank. Moisture collected in the air dryer is expelled with high-pressure air when the compressor reaches cut-out pressure.

Vehicles using air dryers must still have the air tanks drained regularly.

Alcohol evaporator

In cold climates, moisture in the air brake system can freeze and may cause brake failure. Even tiny ice particles can cause problems. An alcohol evaporator adds an alcohol vapor to the air that will mix with any moisture or ice present and reduce its tendency to freeze. Only products specifically designed for this use may be put into an alcohol evaporator.

Diagram 2-6: **Air Dryer**

Air pressure gauge

All vehicles equipped with air brakes must have air pressure gauges that work. Located on the vehicle's instrument panel, the air pressure gauges let you know how much air pressure is in the air brake system to ensure the system is operating normally. Vehicles may use two separate gauges that show primary and secondary air tank pressure or they may be combined in one gauge with two needles. (See Diagram 2-7.) Labelling of air pressure gauges varies and some vehicles have additional air pressure gauges for other systems. Gauges may use metric (kPa) or imperial (psi) measurements on their displays.

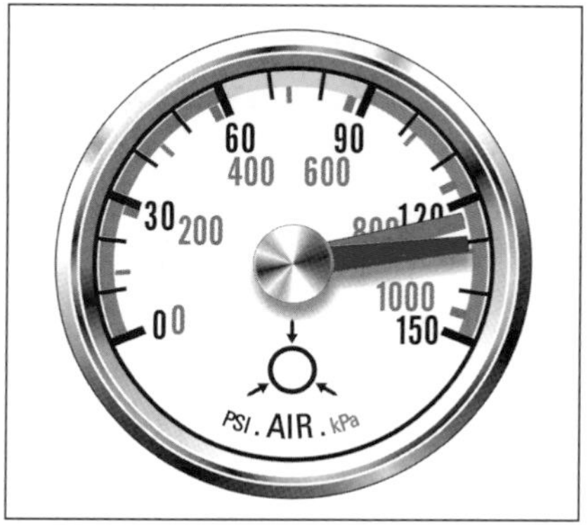

Safety valve

The supply tank and air dryer (if present) usually have safety valves to prevent overpressure of the system. If the governor fails to signal the compressor to cut-out and too much pressure builds up, the safety valves will open to allow the excess air pressure to escape. Safety valves normally open at 1035 kPa (150 psi).

Important: A safety valve that is venting air means there is too much pressure building in the system, requiring immediate repair.

Diagram 2-7: Air pressure gauge showing primary and secondary tank pressure.

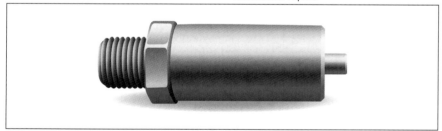

Diagram 2-8: Safety valve

Low air pressure warning devices

When air pressure in either the primary or secondary tank falls below the minimum amount required to bring the vehicle to a safe stop, a warning device on the instrument panel will alert the driver to the danger. The warning device must activate before pressure in either tank falls to 380 kPa (55 psi), although most warning devices activate at 414 kPa (60 psi) or even higher. Low air pressure warning devices must give a visual warning such as a light and may also use a warning buzzer, bell or alarm.

Some vehicles have a warning device called a wig wag. When air pressure is too low, the arm drops into the driver's view.

Important: A low air pressure warning means there is a serious air brake system safety hazard. Bring your vehicle to a safe stop as soon as possible.

Diagram 2-9: Low air pressure warning device

Compressed air can be hazardous

It is important to know that the compressed air that is used in air brake systems can be hazardous if you get near it when it is being exhausted from the vehicle. Compressed air leaving the vehicle travels at a very high speed and will carry moisture, oil, dirt and dust. This can be harmful to the eyes and hearing of anyone in its direct path. Dust, dirt, debris or moisture will spray back up from the ground when the compressed air hits it.

To avoid being in the direct path of air exhausting from the air brake system, you should be familiar with all the places where the compressed air exhausts. These include:

- exhaust ports of brake valves,
- on or near the vehicle's axles,
- air dryer exhaust port, and
- air tank drain valves when tanks are being drained.

Never attempt to dismantle, remove, repair or tamper with any brake system component.

Key Points To Remember

- Compressed air is a form of stored energy that can be hazardous.
- Air compressors compress air by forcing it into a smaller space.
- Air compressors are powered directly by the engine or by using belts and pulleys.
- Air compressors are mounted directly on the engine or by brackets and fasteners.
- The governor controls the air compressor cut-in and cut-out pressure.
- The operating pressure range for vehicle air brake systems must be between 552 kPa and 932 kPa (80 psi and 135 psi).
- It is unsafe to drive a vehicle when the air pressure is outside the normal operating range.
- Compressed air is stored in the vehicle's supply or 'wet' tank and the dual service (primary and secondary) air tanks.
- To prevent too much moisture and oil from collecting, the air tanks must be drained regularly.
- Air pressure gauges indicate air pressure in the vehicle's dual service (primary and secondary) air tanks.
- Safety valves prevent overpressure of the air brake system.
- Low air pressure warning devices give drivers a visual, and sometimes audible, warning that air pressure is dangerously low.
- An air dryer removes moisture from the air brake system and expels it when the compressor reaches cut-out pressure.
- An alcohol evaporator adds alcohol vapor to the air brake system to help prevent moisture in the system from freezing.

Chapter 3

Vehicles with air brakes must have separate brake systems for normal stopping and for parking and emergency braking. These systems are controlled independently. The brakes that are used for normal stopping are called service brakes. This chapter explains the operation and function of the service brake subsystem.

Note: There are circuit diagrams showing service brake system components on page 82 to 84.

Brake pedal operation

Pressing the brake pedal operates the brakes used for normal stopping. The brake pedal also controls the air pressure applied to the service brakes. As the pedal is pressed downward, compressed air passes through a valve attached to the brake pedal and is delivered to the brakes at the wheels. As the brake pedal is pressed harder, the valve opens further, delivering higher air pressure to the service brakes and increasing the braking force at the wheels.

Since most brake system designs use dual circuits, air is drawn from both the primary and secondary tanks and is directed to specific wheels on the vehicle. The wheels that receive air through the primary or secondary circuits vary, depending on the vehicle manufacturer. The dual circuit design means that if one circuit fails, the brakes will still operate on the wheels connected to the other circuit.

Front wheel-limiting valve

It is important to be able to maintain steering control while stopping. When stopping on slippery surfaces, the front wheels may lock, causing you to lose steering ability. To prevent this from happening, many vehicles

have a front wheel-limiting valve that reduces the force of the service brakes on the front steering axle by about half the force on the other brakes.

Most current vehicle designs use automatic valves that drivers cannot control. They reduce air pressure to the front brakes during normal stops and restore full pressure in severe braking situations. This ensures full vehicle braking is available from all wheels during emergency stops.

On older vehicles, the front wheel-limiting valve is operated manually by setting a control on the instrument panel depending on road conditions. In the dry road position, air pressure to the front brakes is not reduced.

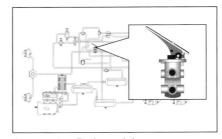

Diagram 3-1: Brake pedal

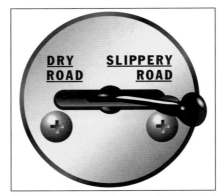

Diagram 3-2: Control for manually-operated front wheel-limiting valve

Brake hoses and tubes

The delivery of compressed air to all components of the air brake system requires a variety of flexible brake hoses and tubes. These are made from a wide range of natural and synthetic materials in various colours, sizes and styles. Each hose and tube must be the correct size and type. Manufacturers currently follow an industry colour code, but this is not the case with older vehicles.

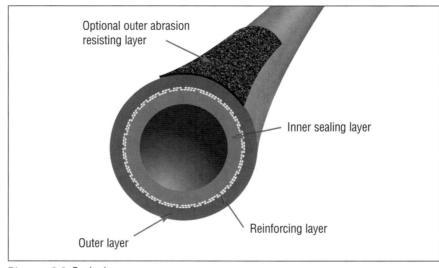

Optional outer abrasion resisting layer

Inner sealing layer

Reinforcing layer

Outer layer

Diagram 3-3: Brake hose

Air brake chambers

Air brake chambers are round metal containers, located at each wheel, where compressed air is converted into mechanical force to apply the brakes and stop the vehicle. There are two kinds of air brake chambers — service and spring brake chambers. A service brake chamber contains a flexible rubber disc called a diaphragm, a metal rod called a pushrod and a return spring. When you press the brake pedal, compressed air fills the service brake chamber, causing the diaphragm to move and pushing out the pushrod to apply the brakes. When air pressure is released, the pushrod is returned to its original position by the spring inside the chamber.

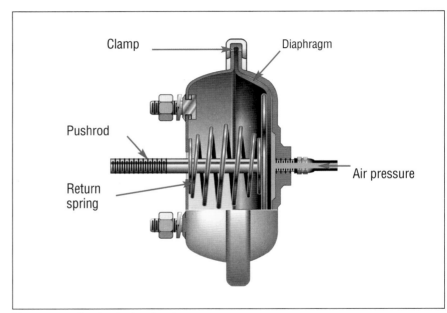

Diagram 3-4: **Service brake chamber**

The pushrod and a lever — called a slack adjuster — link the brake chamber to the brake assembly (which contains the brake drum or disc). When you press the brake pedal, the pushrod extends further from the brake chamber, moving the slack adjuster forward. The motion of the slack adjuster transfers to the brake assembly, causing the brake shoes or pads to make contact with the brake drum or disc.

This action of the pushrod extending from the brake chamber is called pushrod stroke and stroke length is the distance that the pushrod travels out of the chamber. In the most common brake designs, some of the brake linkage — the components linking the brake chamber to the brake assembly — is exposed. As a result, the length of pushrod stroke can be measured and compared to the prescribed adjustment limits for that size, type and style of brake chamber.

The pushrod stroke is dependent on the pressure of the compressed air that enters the brake chamber. For example, when application pressure increases from 69 kPa (10 psi) to 552 kPa (80 psi), the stroke increases noticeably.

Due to the design of brake chambers, each has a limited pushrod stroke length capacity, beyond which no brake force is produced. The brake linkage includes an adjustment device to adjust the position of the brake chamber in relation to the position of the brake shoes. As brakes wear, the linkage must be re-adjusted to ensure the pushrod stroke is always within its normal operating range. This type of brake re-adjustment is required at regular intervals.

Since the drop in brake force can be significant when stroke exceeds the adjustment limits of a brake chamber, it is critical that brakes are correctly adjusted to ensure brake function is retained. The Ontario Highway Traffic Act and regulations strictly regulate brake chamber pushrod stroke. Any brake exceeding the adjustment limit is a defect that requires prompt attention.

NOTE: Only certified technicians may perform brake re-adjustments on manual and automatic slack adjusters. For more information, see Chapter 11, Inspecting Air Brake Adjustment.

Brake chambers are made in a variety of styles, types and sizes, so it is important to correctly identify the brake type and the chamber size to determine the corresponding brake adjustment limit.

Almost all commercial vehicles use a type of brake chamber that is held together by a clamp assembly. These are called clamp-type brake chambers. There is an adjustment chart for these types of chambers on page 85. However, some vehicles may use other types of brake chambers. For adjustment limits for other types of chambers, refer to the Ontario Highway Traffic Act and regulations.

Key Points To Remember

- The brake pedal is used to apply the service brakes.
- Front wheel-limiting valves reduce the force of the service brakes on the front steering axle.
- Pushrod stroke is produced by compressed air entering the brake chamber.
- Each brake chamber style, type and size has a specific pushrod stroke adjustment limit.
- You must not let the pushrod stroke exceed the adjustment limit.

Chapter 4

Spring brakes are designed to work when you are parking your vehicle or in an emergency when your service brakes fail. This chapter explains the operation and function of the spring brake subsystem.

Note: There are circuit diagrams showing spring brake system components on pages 82 to 84.

Spring brakes for emergency braking and parking

All vehicles with air brakes must have a way of stopping if the service brake system fails. Most vehicle manufacturers combine this emergency braking system with a parking brake system using spring brakes.

Spring brakes are not air applied like service brakes. They apply when air pressure leaves the brake chamber and release when air pressure builds up in the chamber.

Spring brakes use a different type of brake chamber from service brakes. A brake chamber that includes both service brake and spring brake sections is called a spring brake chamber. (See Diagram 4-1.) Spring brake chambers apply the brakes by means of a large coil spring that provides enough force to hold the brakes in the applied position, instead of using air to apply the brakes.

Spring brake chambers are different in appearance from service brake chambers. To accommodate the large coil spring, a section must be added to the service brake chamber that is clearly visible and adds significantly to its size. The spring brake section is 'piggy-backed' onto the service brake section and these two sections function as two separate chambers. The portion nearest the pushrod end is the service brake section and it works in the same manner as a separately mounted service brake chamber.

To release the spring brakes, normally about 414 kPa (60 psi) of air pressure must be supplied to the spring brake chamber to compress or 'cage' the spring. If system pressure is below 414 kPa (60 psi), the spring brakes start applying because there is no longer enough pressure to keep them released. (Note that this number may depend on the age of the brakes, newer brakes may require 90 -95 psi before they release, and older brakes may take as little as 35 psi to release.)

Many vehicles can still be driven even with the spring brakes applied because the spring brakes do not have the braking power of the full service brake application. Before driving the vehicle, it is important to ensure that the air brake system has enough air pressure (normally 414 kPa (60 psi)) to keep the spring brakes from applying. Due to the way

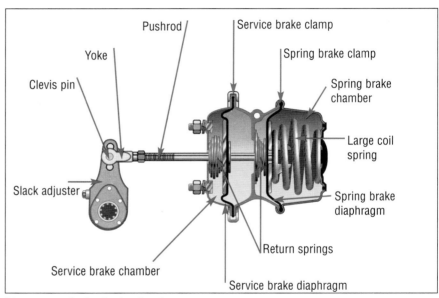

Diagram 4-1: **Spring brake chamber**

most spring brake chambers are currently constructed, it is very difficult to unintentionally release the spring.

The large coil spring used in the spring brake chamber is compressed under very high tension. Tampering, damage or corrosion can cause the spring to release, resulting in sudden violent motion of parts of the air brake chamber. Since this can be hazardous, never attempt to service or repair any air brake chamber.

Disabling the spring brake chamber

Using a 'caging bolt' or other mechanism, a technician can manually compress or 'cage' the spring in a spring brake chamber. This may be necessary to move a vehicle in an emergency. When a spring brake chamber fails, a technician may use the manual caging method to temporarily disable a spring brake chamber. A spring brake chamber that has been disabled by this method looks different and the parking and emergency brake will not apply. Disabled or caged spring brake chambers can be recognized by the protrusion of the caging bolt or other similar mechanism. Drivers encountering a disabled spring brake chamber

should have the vehicle inspected and repaired immediately.

Spring brake (parking and emergency) control valves

A spring brake control valve is normally a push/pull type valve fitted with a yellow, four-sided knob located near the driver. Most spring brake control valves are pushed to supply air and release the spring brakes, then pulled to exhaust air and apply the spring brakes. Some vehicles may have this function reversed, but its functions are normally described on or near the control valve. Some vehicles use a toggle type valve for this purpose. Drivers must be familiar with the type of control valve used in their vehicle.

Some trucks and tractors may also have a separate control called a tractor parking brake control valve to release the spring brakes on the tractor while keeping the trailer spring brakes applied. This

Diagram 4-2: Spring brake control valve

optional control valve normally has a round blue knob.

Spring brake control valves are designed to respond to air brake system pressure dropping below a certain level (normally 414 kPa or 60 psi) by exhausting the remaining air that is holding the spring brakes in the released position. This causes sudden automatic application of the spring brakes and an uncontrolled vehicle stop.

The control valve knob will pop out when this occurs.

Important: If air brake system pressure drops below its normal operating range (normally 414 kPa or 60 psi), the spring brakes will automatically begin to apply.

In an emergency when the service brakes fail, the spring brakes can be applied by using the spring brake control valve.

The effectiveness of a vehicle's spring brakes depends on the condition of the brakes and proper brake adjustment. If brakes are out of adjustment, the spring brakes may not stop or hold a vehicle stationary.

Remember: Poor brake adjustment reduces the ability of service brakes to stop a vehicle and reduces the ability of spring brakes to stop or hold a vehicle.

DD3 brake chamber

Many buses and motor coaches are fitted with parking and emergency brakes that do not use a large spring in the brake chamber. This type of chamber is called a DD3 Safety Actuator. Although similar to a spring brake chamber, a DD3 brake chamber has three air line connections instead of two. Internally, these chambers have a mechanical means of locking a brake in the applied position. A control valve similar to the one used in conventional spring brake systems applies the emergency and parking brakes. Releasing the spring brakes requires operating the control valve and then pressing the brake pedal for three to five seconds.

Key Points To Remember
- The brake pedal is used to apply the service brakes.
- Spring brake chambers include both service brake and spring brake sections.
- The large coil spring inside a spring brake chamber is under high tension and can be hazardous.
- When the spring in a spring brake chamber is compressed or 'caged', it looks different and the spring brake will not apply.
- A spring brake control valve is normally a push/pull type valve fitted with a yellow, four-sided knob located near the driver.
- When the air brake system pressure falls below its normal operating range (normally 414 kPa or 60 psi), the spring brakes will begin to apply automatically.
- If brakes are out of adjustment, the spring brakes may not stop or hold a vehicle.

The trailer brake subsystem includes components and features on both the trailer and the truck or tractor that tows it. This chapter explains the major components of the trailer brake subsystem and how they work.

Note: There is a circuit diagram of a trailer brake subsystem on page 84. For trailer brake components on the towing vehicle, see the circuit diagram on page 83.

Trailer brake components

The air brake system on a trailer includes air tanks and automatic spring brake applications. Vehicles that are designed to tow trailers must be fitted with additional valves used only for the trailer. The brake system of a converter dolly that attaches one trailer to another is essentially the same as a trailer system.

Connecting a trailer

Two connections must be made to join a trailer's brake system to the brake system of the towing vehicle. One connection carries air to fill the trailer's tanks and is called the supply or emergency line. The other carries pressure for the service brakes and is called the service line. Two pairs of metal trailer couplers or 'gladhands' are used to make these connections. Each coupler includes a flexible seal that provides a leak-free connection. These couplers must be kept clean and in good condition.

Most towing vehicles have receptacles called 'dead end' or 'dummy' couplers that protect the couplers from dirt and water when not in use.

To connect the couplers, the surfaces that contain the seal are placed at an angle against one another. Rotating them into

alignment completes the connection. Once correctly joined, the connectors lock together and considerable effort is needed to pull them apart.

Since there are two air lines to the trailer and the design of the supply and service couplers are basically the same, there is a possibility of cross-connecting the lines. In most cases, the trailer couplers are colour-coded during manufacturing — red for the supply line and blue for the service line. By matching these colours, the lines are properly connected. To further prevent cross-connections, most couplers are designed so that they will only fit onto the matching coupler. Some couplers, however, have no features to prevent cross-connection.

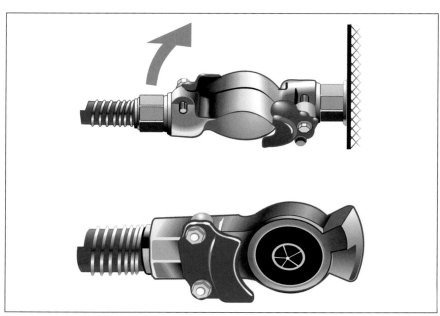

Diagram 5-1: **Trailer couplers or 'gladhands'**

Trailer couplers or 'gladhands'

When trailer lines are cross-connected the trailer brakes will not work correctly — the spring brakes may not release, the towing vehicle may lose air and the service brakes will not function properly. It is not safe to operate a vehicle with cross-connected trailer lines.

A towing vehicle can pull more than one trailer. To connect trailers to each other, additional supply and service connectors at the rear of a trailer must be the same as those used on the towing vehicle. To prevent air loss from these lines when they are not in use, the lines are usually equipped with manual shut-off valves. Drivers must be familiar with the proper use of these vehicles before operating them.

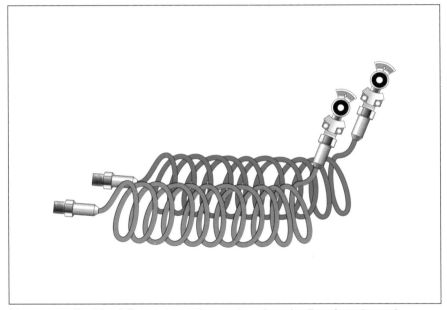

Diagram 5-2: Flexible air lines connect the supply and service lines from the towing vehicle to the trailer.

Applying trailer service brakes

The trailer service brakes will apply whenever the brake pedal is pressed. Often, a hand valve is also fitted on the steering column or the instrument panel of the towing vehicle so the driver can apply the trailer service brakes independent of the towing vehicle's brakes. When the hand valve and brake pedal are used at the same time, the trailer will receive the higher pressure. Using the brake pedal or hand valve sends air pressure through the trailer service line.

Trailer hand valves must never be used for parking or emergency stops.

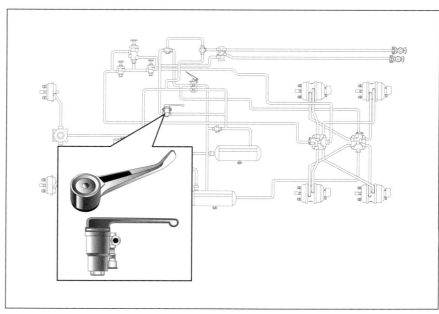

Diagram 5-3: Hand valve

Trailer supply valve

The trailer supply valve is usually a push/pull type valve near the driver that supplies air to the trailer's brake system through the supply line. This valve normally has a red, eight-sided knob that the driver pushes in to open and supply air to the trailer and pulls out to close or when no trailer is attached.

Failing to close the trailer supply valve when there is no trailer attached allows a large amount of air to escape from the towing vehicle's air brake system. To prevent all of the air from being lost, the trailer supply valve is designed to close automatically. If the valve is open and air escapes or if the trailer breaks loose from the towing vehicle, the valve closes automatically when air pressure in the trailer supply line drops to between 138 and 311 kPa (20 and 45 psi).

Because there is a large amount of air flowing out of the trailer

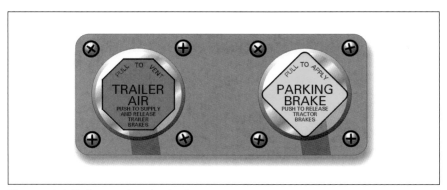

Diagram 5-4: Trailer supply valve (red)

supply line, the pressure in the line will be considerably lower than the pressure in the air tanks. This means that in most cases the valve will close automatically well before the pressure displayed on the air pressure gauges reads between 138 and 311 kPa (20 and 45 psi).

In an emergency when the trailer service brakes fail, the trailer spring brakes can be applied by using the trailer supply valve.

Tractor (towing vehicle) protection valve

Once the trailer supply valve closes, the tractor protection valve on the towing vehicle also closes. This prevents air loss out of the towing vehicle when there is no trailer attached. The trailer supply valve controls the tractor protection valve. When the trailer supply valve is opened to allow air to the trailer, air pressure is also directed to open the tractor protection valve and allow air to the trailer service line. When the trailer supply valve is closed, air pressure exhausts from the tractor protection valve and it closes by spring force. When the tractor protection valve is closed, air enters the valve but does not pass through it.

Automatic spring (parking and emergency) brakes

Trailer brake subsystems use both service brakes for normal braking and spring brakes for parking and emergency braking. The spring brakes must apply automatically when the air pressure in the trailer supply line drops below 414 kPa (60 psi).

The air pressure may drop due to one of the following:
- the driver parks the vehicle and closes (pulls out) the trailer supply valve; or
- the trailer supply line ruptures or becomes disconnected for some reason.

Spring brake or service brake priority

Instead of providing air pressure to both the service brakes and the spring brakes at the same time, trailer brake subsystems give priority to one or the other. This means that in a system with 'spring brake priority', the air from the towing vehicle first fills the air tank for the spring brakes to a certain pressure before filling the air tank for the service brakes. Most manufacturers have changed the trailer spring brake valves on spring brake priority systems such that if there is air loss to the service brakes the spring brakes will lose sufficient air that they will begin to apply.

Trailers with 'service brake priority' fill the service brake air tank before filling the spring brake air tank.

Trailers with spring brake priority can be towed without waiting for the service brake air

tanks to fill. This means a trailer could be on the road without enough air pressure to operate its service brakes. This is not the case in a trailer with service brake priority, which ensures that enough air is available to operate the service brakes before the spring brakes can be released and the trailer can be towed.

If there is a loss of air to the trailer service brakes in a spring brake priority system, the spring brakes may remain released while no service brakes are available on the trailer. The only way to apply brakes on the trailer is to close the trailer supply valve to cause the trailer's spring brakes to apply automatically.

Consult your employer or a qualified person to assist you in determining whether a trailer uses a spring brake or service brake priority system.

Key Points To Remember

- The air brake subsystem of a trailer includes air tanks and automatic spring brake application.
- Trailer couplers or 'gladhands' are used to connect the air brake system of the towing vehicle to the air brake system of the trailer.
- In most cases, trailer couplers can be identified by their colour and are designed to prevent cross-connection.
- When trailer couplers are cross-connected, the trailer service and spring brakes will not function correctly.
- The trailer hand valve is used to apply the trailer service brakes independent of the towing vehicle's brakes.
- The trailer supply valve is usually a push/pull type valve near the driver that supplies air to the trailer's brake system through the supply line.
- The tractor protection valve prevents air loss from the towing vehicle.
- When air pressure in the trailer supply line drops below 414 kPa (60 psi), the trailer spring brakes will apply automatically.
- In an emergency when the trailer service brakes fail, the trailer spring brakes can be applied by using the trailer supply valve.
- A trailer with a 'spring brake priority' system will allow the trailer spring brakes to release before the trailer service brakes have enough pressure to operate.

Chapter 6

FOUNDATION BRAKES

Drivers of vehicles with air brakes must be familiar with the function and appearance of the various types of foundation brake assemblies, and be able to inspect the components for safety defects. This chapter explains the components of common foundation brakes and how they work.

Types of foundation brakes

The brake assembly components at the wheels of a vehicle are generally called the foundation components because they form the basis on which the rest of the system is built. Foundation components are the mechanical parts contained in or around the wheels that are operated by the air brake system. An air brake system can be designed to work with several designs of foundation brake subsystems — even on the same vehicle.

There are three types of foundation brake systems — 'S' cam brakes, disc brakes and wedge brakes.

'S' cam brakes

The 'S' cam brake is the most common type of foundation brake used on commercial vehicles with air brake systems. This is a drum brake that uses air brake chambers and linkage to press the brake shoes against the surface of the brake drum. The stroke of the air brake chamber pushrod acts on the slack adjuster attached to the end of the camshaft. Pushrod stroke causes the camshaft to rotate. The 'S' shape on one end of the camshaft forces the brake shoes apart and against the brake drum.

Many of the parts of an 'S' cam brake are located in the wheel. Characteristic of the 'S' cam brake design is the exposed pushrod. This allows easy access to the brake linkage to check brake adjustment. The components within the wheel are difficult to see, particularly when a dust shield or backing plate is used to protect the components.

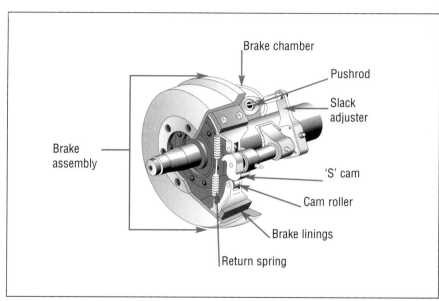

Diagram 6-1: 'S' cam brake

The brake shoes and drum are located within the wheel, along with the hardware to hold these parts in position.

Other internal parts may include some or all of the following:

- A brake spider that serves as the main mounting base for the brake shoes

- Single or dual anchor pins to attach one end of the brake shoes
- Anchor springs to hold the brake shoes in position at the anchor end
- The head of the 'S' camshaft
- Camshaft rollers that rotate with the camshaft while moving the brake shoes inward and outward
- A return spring to pull the brake shoes in to the released position and keep the camshaft rollers engaged with the camshaft head

The external components are much easier to see and identify. They include:

- Brake chamber and mounting brackets
- Slack adjuster
- Pushrod
- The shaft portion of the 'S' camshaft
- Support brackets and bushings for the camshaft
- Dust shields or backing plates
- Brake drums

Disc brakes

The disc air brake system also uses both external and internal components, but there are fewer components involved. All disc air brakes use calipers and rotors. The brake rotor is only partially visible because the wheel, caliper and dust shields usually cover parts of it. Disc brake designs use brake chambers that may have exposed linkage and a slack adjuster. Brake chamber pushrod stroke presses the brake pads against the rotor.

Diagram 6-2: **Disc brake**

Wedge brakes

The wedge air brake system is a type of drum brake that includes brake drums and shoes with no exposed brake linkage. Air brake chambers are mounted so that their pushrods face inward toward the brake shoes and drum. The stroke of the brake chamber pushrod slides a wedge between the brake shoes, forcing them outward against the drum. Wedge air brakes are designed to be self-adjusting.

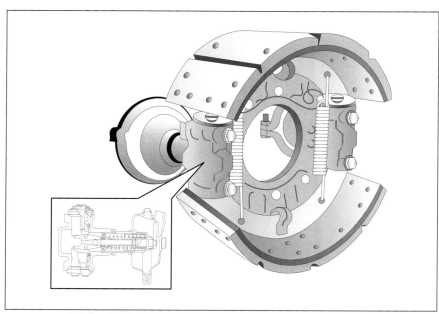

Diagram 6-3: Wedge brake

Key Points To Remember

- Components of 'S' cam air brakes include brake drums, brake shoes and linings, camshafts, pushrods, cam support brackets, spiders, rollers, return springs, dust shields and backing plates, slack adjusters and brake chambers.
- Components of disc air brakes include rotors, calipers, brake pads, slack adjusters and brake chambers.
- Components of wedge air brakes include brake drums, brake shoes and linings, spiders, dust shields and brake chambers.

Chapter 7

Several factors affect how your vehicle's brakes work. These include the speed and weight of your vehicle, brake adjustment and anti-lock braking systems. This chapter explains the demand these factors place on the brake system while driving and what actions you should take to make sure your brakes work effectively.

Vehicle speed and weight

Increasing how much weight your vehicle carries or how fast you drive increases the demand on your brake system. As the demand on the brake system increases, the brakes must do more work. In an air brake system, this means greater brake application pressure will be needed to meet the higher demand. To achieve this, you must press the brake pedal further.

As vehicle speed increases, the demand on brakes increases at a rate that is greater than the change in speed. For example, when speed is doubled, the demand on the brakes increases by four times. (See Diagram 7-1.)

Brake systems are designed for use on vehicles that are loaded within their rated capacity. Exceeding the weight capacity of a vehicle places abnormal demands on its brake system. Vehicle weight affects the brake system in the following ways:

• The demand on brakes will increase in proportion to any increase in vehicle weight. (See Diagram 7-2.)

• It is possible to exceed the capacity of a vehicle's braking system by loading a vehicle with more weight than it is rated to carry.

• When a vehicle is overloaded, the brake system may not be able to safely stop the vehicle.

When considering a vehicle's stopping distance, many factors must be taken into account. Stopping distance can be calculated based on time and vehicle speed. A split-second delay in brake application and release ranging up to one-half second is present

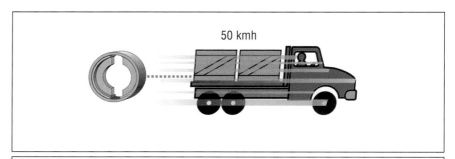

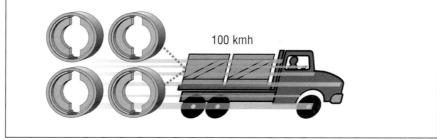

Diagram 7-1: Your vehicle's brakes must do more work when you drive faster.

in all air brake systems. This delay must be taken into account when determining suitable following distances and appropriate action during vehicle stops.

Brakes create heat

Brakes convert the energy of a moving vehicle into heat. The frequency and type of brake use determines how much heat is created. When brakes are used repeatedly — such as when travelling down a long or steep hill or driving in stop-and-go traffic — or when severe braking takes place, the operating temperature of the brakes can become higher than normal. In some cases, brake temperatures can become so severe they cause damage to brake components.

Driving habits affect the amount of heat that develops in the brakes. Good driving habits include anticipating road conditions and leaving enough time to stop. In particular, keeping a safe distance behind other

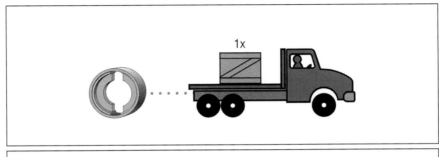

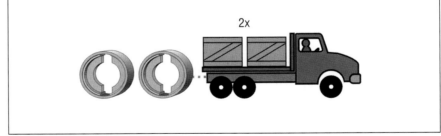

Diagram 7-2: Your vehicle's brakes must do more work when your vehicle carries more weight.

vehicles reduces the incidence of harsh brake use and excessive heat build-up in the brakes.

Some vehicles use engine brakes, retarders or auxiliary brakes — fitted onto drive lines that use engine compression, hydraulic or electric means — to slow a vehicle and assist in avoiding excessive brake temperature.

Brake fade

As brake components heat up, you may experience a reduction in their effectiveness and find that you need to press harder on the brake pedal to develop enough brake force. This is known as brake fade and it is more noticeable on some vehicles than others.

In extreme cases, such as travelling down a long hill at excessive speed or with an overloaded vehicle, brake fade can become so severe and result in such a significant loss of brake force, that you may be unable to slow or stop your vehicle.

Brakes must be adjusted correctly

Full brake capacity is not often needed during normal conditions. However, for safety, the full capacity of the brake system must always be available.

The brake force produced at a wheel drops significantly when the stroke of its brake chamber pushrod becomes excessive. When pushrod stroke becomes excessive, the vehicle loses some of its ability to stop. (See Diagram 7-3.) It is unlikely that you will notice a small loss of braking ability during normal driving. It may only become evident when higher demands are placed on the brakes such as heavier loads, higher speeds, long downhill grades or emergency stops.

When brake chamber pushrod stroke exceeds the adjustment limit, braking ability can be reduced so much that the brakes may not stop or hold the vehicle. Brakes must be kept properly adjusted to ensure

each chamber pushrod stroke is within its adjustment limit.

Remember: Proper brake adjustment ensures that the brake chamber always produces the necessary brake force. When a brake is out of adjustment — when pushrod stroke exceeds the adjustment limit — braking ability is reduced.

The Ontario Highway Traffic Act and regulations require vehicles with air brakes to be checked at least once each day to ensure correct brake adjustment. Adjustment limits are prescribed for each style, size and type of air brake chamber (See chart on page 85.) The pushrod stroke of each air brake chamber must not exceed its adjustment limit. Vehicles have full braking ability only when all brakes are properly adjusted.

Brakes that are out of adjustment cannot be detected except by a reliable inspection method.

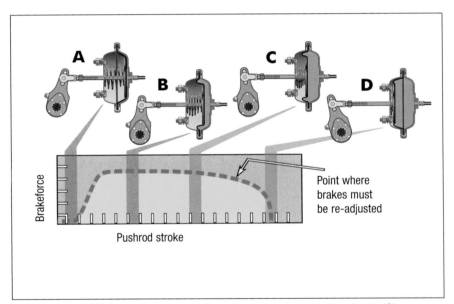

Diagram 7-3: At 'A', the brake is released and no air pressure has entered the brake chamber. No brake force is being produced. At 'B', air pressure enters the brake chamber. The brake chamber produces mechanical force and a small amount of pushrod stroke. At 'C', more air pressure is entering the chamber, producing even more pushrod stroke. At 'D', pushrod stroke has exceeded the adjustment limit and no brake force is produced.

Anti-lock braking systems

When a wheel locks and a tire skids, a vehicle loses steering control and directional stability. Under certain driving conditions, you may find it difficult to get the brake force you want without causing one or more of the wheels to lock. Anti-lock braking systems, which are also called ABS, are designed to sense the speed of the wheels on a vehicle. An abnormal drop in wheel speed, which indicates potential wheel lock, causes the brake force to be reduced to that wheel. This is how the anti-lock braking system prevents tire skid and the accompanying loss of steering control. This improves vehicle safety during heavy brake use or when braking with poor traction.

Although anti-lock braking systems help to prevent wheel lock, you should not expect the stopping distance for your vehicle to be shortened. Under normal driving conditions, on clean dry roads, you will notice no difference between vehicles with anti-lock braking and vehicles without anti-lock braking.

Vehicles with anti-lock braking systems use warning indicator lights or malfunction lamps to indicate the status of the system and warn of malfunctions. These indicator lights are mounted on the dashboard or driver console. On trailers, the indicators are usually mounted in locations that make them visible in your rear-view mirror. You should be familiar with the location of anti-lock braking system indicators on your vehicle and how they work.

Important: If an anti-lock braking system malfunction occurs, regular brake function is still available.

Diagram 7-4

Key Points To Remember
- The demands on the brake system increase as vehicle speed or weight increases.
- Overloading a vehicle can cause it to lose its braking ability.
- Repeated or severe use of brakes causes higher brake temperatures.
- High brake temperatures can cause the vehicle's braking ability to fade.
- When brakes are out of adjustment — when pushrod stroke exceeds the adjustment limit — braking ability is reduced.
- Anti-lock braking systems (ABS) help maintain steering control during emergency braking.
- Anti-lock braking systems help to prevent wheel lock but do not shorten vehicle stopping distance.
- Warning indicator lights are used with anti-lock braking systems to indicate system malfunctions.

Chapter 8

Drivers of vehicles with air brakes must understand and comply with the Ontario Highway Traffic Act and regulations, as well as general safety issues. These are outlined in this chapter. In addition, this chapter explains what to do when you find a defect in the air brake system.

Safety standards for commercial vehicles

The Ontario Highway Traffic Act and regulations provide specific requirements for the safe operation of commercial motor vehicles. When vehicles fail to comply with these requirements, the driver, operator and owner of the vehicle must ensure that the vehicle is not driven on any road or highway. Operating a vehicle that does not comply with the Ontario Highway Traffic Act and regulations is an offence that carries penalties. These may range from a fine to vehicle detainment or impoundment.

Important: Operating a vehicle with defects or failing to conduct the required inspections can result in charges against the driver and/or operator, as well as detainment or impoundment of the vehicle.

Safety concerns while inspecting air brake systems

When conducting an inspection of the air brake system, be sure to take the following precautions to avoid potential hazards:
- Park on a level surface to keep the vehicle from rolling. Inspection of the air brake system requires certain steps to be completed with the parking brakes released. A level surface will reduce the possibility of unexpected vehicle movement.
- Park away from traffic and other hazards to provide a safe work area around the vehicle to conduct the inspection.

- Turn off the engine. Moving parts within the engine compartment pose safety hazards, so inspections should always be performed with the engine stopped.
- Secure the vehicle with wheel chocks or blocks to prevent vehicle movement during the inspection. (See Diagram 8-1.) Wheel chocks or blocks must be used whenever a test or inspection procedure requires the driver to leave the driver's seat with the parking brakes released.
- Avoid getting in the direct path or immediate area of compressed air exhausting from air brake system components.

Remember: Inspections of vehicles with air brakes must be completed at regular intervals to ensure they comply with the Ontario Highway Traffic Act and regulations. Drivers are required by law to report any defects of the air brake system to the vehicle operator.

Diagram 8-1: Correct position of wheel chocks

Key Points To Remember

- Vehicles with air brakes must comply with the Ontario Highway Traffic Act and regulations. If a vehicle does not comply, both the driver and the operator may be charged.
- When conducting an inspection, make sure the vehicle is parked on a level surface, in a secure manner and in a safe location.
- Wheel chocks or blocks should be used to prevent vehicle movement during an inspection.
- During an inspection, drivers must be cautious of moving vehicle parts and compressed air exhausting from the vehicle.
- The Ontario Highway Traffic Act and regulations prohibit the driving or operation of a vehicle with a defective air brake system on any road or highway.

Chapter 9

Drivers of vehicles with air brakes must be able to inspect and identify defects in the air brake system components according to the Ontario Highway Traffic Act and regulations. This chapter explains how to carry out the inspection.

Inspecting the brake system

Completing an inspection of an air brake system mainly involves looking to see that each brake component is free from apparent defects or problems and that there is no evidence of any abnormality. This type of inspection is limited to those components that are visible to the driver.

Some defects are more difficult to detect than others. To carry out inspections effectively, drivers must be aware of the possible defective conditions that can exist and the evidence of their presence.

Inspecting foundation brake components

Begin by inspecting the foundation brake components for damage caused by debris, component failure or deterioration. Drivers are expected to identify brake components that are damaged, missing or malfunctioning. To detect these defects, you must be familiar with the normal appearance of the foundation brake components and the signs of present or impending defects.

Check brake lining to drum contact

For the brakes to work, the brake shoe lining must be pressed against the brake drum when brakes are applied and be out of contact with the drum when brakes are released. Lining that does not contact the drum when the brakes are applied indicates a malfunctioning brake. (See Diagram 9-1.)

51

Check brake lining conditions

Brake lining is the friction material that is fastened to the metal brake shoe. For the brake to work properly, the lining must be in good condition and remain securely attached to the shoe. Brake lining that is noticeably cracked, loose or missing is defective.

Check brake lining contamination

Within the wheel assembly are components that require lubrication. When problems develop within the wheel, some of the lubricant may escape and come into contact with the brake lining. When grease or oil is present on the brake lining, abnormal brake behaviour will result. Brake lining that is contaminated with grease or oil is defective.

Check brake lining thickness

Brake linings are manufactured to standard dimensions that allow a considerable portion of the lining to wear before replacement is needed.

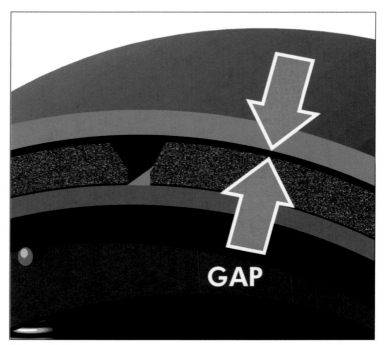

GAP

Diagram 9-1

When the lining becomes worn too thin, there is an increased danger of brake failure and damage to other components. Lining that is less than the prescribed minimum thickness is defective.

An inspection of the foundation brake components includes checking for the following defects:

- brake shoe lining not contacting the brake drum;
- damaged, missing or malfunctioning foundation brake components; and
- cracked, loose, missing or contaminated brake lining, improper drum contact or lining thickness that is less than required.

Important: The Ontario Highway Traffic Act and regulations prohibit the operation of a vehicle with a foundation brake defect on any road or highway.

Inspecting air brake chambers

The size of an air brake chamber is based on the area of the chamber diaphragm in square inches. The brake on each end of an axle should have the same size air brake chamber to ensure brake forces are balanced. This is even more important for steering axles where brake imbalance can affect the steering. Air brake chambers from different manufacturers may look different even if they are the same size.

Air brake chambers must be inspected for air leaks when air pressure is applied to the chamber. This means inspecting the chamber when the spring brakes are released and the service brakes are applied. Air brake chamber air leaks can usually be detected audibly.

Air brake chambers may have vent holes that are visible. These are manufactured holes and are not a concern. Holes or cracks that are caused by impact or other forms of damage mean the air brake chamber is defective.

The brake chamber is connected to the brake assembly by a pushrod, yoke, clevis pin, slack adjuster and camshaft. Slack adjusters act as levers that increase the force of the air brake chambers. Their effective length is critical. Most slack adjusters are designed with two or three holes for attachment of the pushrod. Attaching the slack adjuster using the incorrect hole changes the slack adjuster's effective length. The slack adjuster's effective length is the distance between the centre of the camshaft and the clevis pin. To ensure balanced braking, slack adjusters on each side of an axle should be the same effective lengths. Therefore, when slack adjusters have multiple holes, the pushrods on each side of the axle are usually attached using the same hole.

Some models of slack adjusters use different patterns of holes that can result in a different appearance on each end of an axle, even when they are correctly attached. The distance between the center of the camshaft and the clevis pin must always be the same on each end of a steering axle.

An inspection of a vehicle's air brake chambers includes checking for the following defects:

- audible air leaks;
- cracks and non-manufactured holes;
- mismatched air brake chamber size on a steering axle; and
- mismatched slack adjuster effective length on a steering axle.

Important: The Ontario Highway Traffic Act and regulations prohibit the operation of a vehicle with an air brake chamber defect on any road or highway.

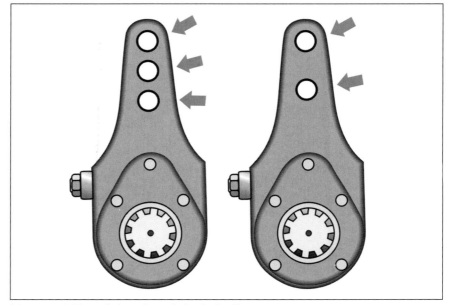

Diagram 9-2: Three-hole and two-hole slack adjusters

Inspecting brake drums and rotors

Wheels, dust shields and other parts of the vehicle may obstruct your view of the brake drums and rotors. Drivers must inspect drums and rotors for damage and signs of cracks or breaks. There is often a noticeable change in the behaviour of brakes with brake drums or rotors that are defective, cracked or broken.

An inspection of a vehicle's brake drums and rotors includes checking for the following defect:

- cracked or broken brake drums or rotors.

Important: The Ontario Highway Traffic Act and regulations prohibit the operation of a vehicle with a brake drum or rotor defect on any road or highway.

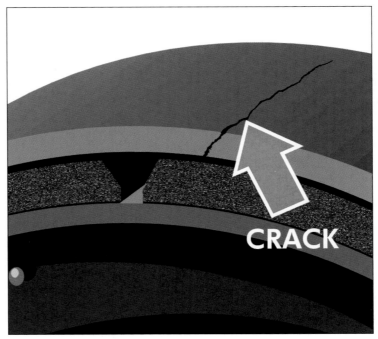

Diagram 9-3: A cracked brake drum

Inspecting brake hoses and tubes

A variety of hoses and tubes make up the air lines used in an air brake system. Some of these air lines are positioned against the vehicle frame and other structural parts. Others that are exposed are more likely to suffer damage.

Hoses and tubes have an inner layer to create an air tight seal, reinforcing fabric layers to provide strength and an outer layer of plastic or rubber for protection. Some may use steel reinforcing layers. Holes or wear in an outer layer may lead to holes in the inner layers. Holes in the inner layers will produce an air leak. Damaged or worn air lines are a concern even if no leak is evident yet.

When damage extends into the reinforcing or inner layer, the air line is defective. In some cases, different colors of material are used to indicate when wear extends through a layer.

Damage or deterioration to brake hoses and tubes may be in the form of wear, cuts, abrasion and heat damage. Air leaks are usually detectable audibly; moving hoses and tubing back and forth often helps to pinpoint a leak.

Air brake systems require the use of fittings specifically designed and approved for use in air brake systems. Using improper fittings, or connecting or repairing air lines by improper means is prohibited.

An inspection of the vehicle's air lines includes checking for the following defects:

- audible air leak;
- damaged or worn air lines; and
- improper fittings used to connect or repair an air line.

Important: The Ontario Highway Traffic Act and regulations prohibit the operation of a vehicle with an air line defect on any road or highway.

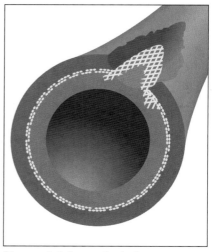

Diagram 9-4: A worn brake hose

Inspecting air tanks

Air tanks must remain securely attached to the vehicle. Check that they are secure both by looking at them and by attempting to move them. In addition to the tanks themselves, check the security of the mounting brackets and hardware that hold the air tanks to the vehicle. Unusual movement may indicate an insecure air tank or mounting bracket.

An inspection of a vehicle's air tanks includes checking for the following defect:

- insecurely mounted air tank.

Important: The Ontario Highway Traffic Act and regulations prohibit the operation of a vehicle with a defective air tank on any road or highway.

Inspecting air compressors

Air compressors must be securely mounted onto the engine and any supports or brackets that are used must also be secure. Air compressors must always be inspected with the engine stopped. If a compressor is belt driven, inspect the condition and tension of the drive pulleys and belt. Drive pulleys must be secure and in good condition. The belt should give slightly when firm hand pressure is applied. Excessive belt movement indicates the belt is too loose. A belt that is loose, cut or frayed is defective.

An inspection of a vehicle's air compressor includes checking for the following defects:

- loose air compressor drive;
- belt pulley;
- loose, cut or frayed air compressor drive belt; and
- insecure air compressor mounting, bracket or fasteners.

Important: The Ontario Highway Traffic Act and regulations prohibit the operation of a vehicle with a defective air compressor, mounting bracket, fasteners or drive belt on any road or highway.

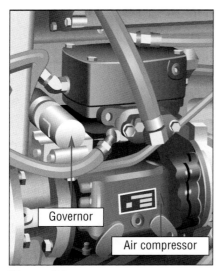

Governor

Air compressor

Diagram 9-5

Key Points To Remember

- When inspecting the foundation brake components, the driver must check for damaged, missing or malfunctioning components; cracked, loose, missing or contaminated brake linings; improper drum contact; and linings that are less than the required thickness.
- When inspecting the air brake chambers, the driver must check for audible air leaks, cracks and non-manufactured holes.
- When inspecting the brake chambers on each side of a steering axle, the driver must check for mismatched slack adjusters and air brake chamber size.
- When inspecting the brake drums and rotors, the driver must check for cracked or broken drums or rotors.
- When inspecting the air brake hoses and tubes that make up the air lines, the driver must check for leaks, damage or wear, as well as improper fittings.
- When inspecting the air tanks, the driver must check for insecure mounting.
- When inspecting the air compressor, the driver must check for a loose, frayed or cut drive belt, as well as insecure mounting bracket or fasteners.

Chapter 10

INSPECTING AIR BRAKE SYSTEM OPERATION

Each time you drive a vehicle with air brakes, you must make sure that there are no defects and that the vehicle complies with the Ontario Highway Traffic Act and regulations. This chapter describes the inspection procedure you must follow. It also prepares you for the Ministry of Transportation air brake endorsement practical examination.

Secure the vehicle before you start

To conduct the inspection, park your vehicle on level ground to prevent it from rolling. Apply the spring brakes and put wheel chocks or blocks in place to secure the vehicle.

Important: Never leave the driver's seat or get under a vehicle unless the vehicle's spring brakes are applied or the wheels are securely blocked.

Testing low air pressure warning devices

To test the low air pressure warning device, pressure in the system must be reduced to the point where the device activates or 380 kPa (55 psi), whichever is higher. The pressure at which the warning device deactivates during a rise in pressure is not necessarily the same point at which it activates during a drop in pressure. Begin the test with the pressure above 621 kPa (90 psi) and the engine stopped or running. With the ignition switch turned on, reduce pressure by repeatedly pressing and releasing the brake pedal.

Observe the air pressure gauges and note when the device activates. Most warning devices will activate above 414 kPa (60 psi). If the warning device fails to activate at a minimum of 380 kPa (55 psi), the low air pressure warning device is defective.

Step-by-step procedure

1. Ensure air brake system pressure is above 621 kPa (90 psi).
2. The engine may be stopped or left running but ignition must be on.
3. Observe the primary and secondary air tank pressure gauges.
4. Press and release the brake pedal repeatedly to lower air pressure.
5. Watch and listen for the low air pressure warning device to activate.
6. When the device activates, note the air pressure displayed by the gauges.

Pass

✓ The vehicle passes the test if the device activates when pressure is at or above 380 kPa (55 psi) on both primary and secondary air tank gauges.

Fail

✗ The vehicle fails the test if the device does not activate or activates when pressure is below 380 kPa (55 psi) on either the primary or secondary air pressure gauge.

Important: The Ontario Highway Traffic Act and regulations prohibit the operation of a vehicle with a defective low air pressure warning device.

Testing air pressure build-up time

The air compressor must be capable of meeting the demand of the air brake system and restoring air brake system pressure to the normal range quickly. This is confirmed by testing whether air pressure rises to a specified level within a specified time.

To test the air pressure build-up time, reduce the system pressure to below 552 kPa (80 psi). If the vehicle has a trailer attached, ensure the trailer supply valve is closed (pulled out). With the engine idling between 600 and 900 rpm, observe the time required for the air pressure to rise from 587 kPa (85 psi) to 690 kPa (100 psi).

If the time required to build up air pressure exceeds two minutes, the air brake system is defective.

Step-by-step procedure

1. Lower air brake system pressure to below 552 kPa (80 psi).
2. Run the engine at 600 to 900 rpm.
3. Observe the primary and secondary air tank pressure gauges.
4. Note the time when pressure reaches the start value of 587 kPa (85 psi).
5. Note the time when pressure reaches the end value of 690 kPa (100 psi).

Pass

✓ Vehicle passes the test if pressure build-up time is equal to or less than two minutes.

Fail

✗ Vehicle fails the test if pressure build-up time is greater than two minutes.

Important: The Ontario Highway Traffic Act and regulations prohibit operation of a vehicle that fails to build air pressure within the prescribed time.

Testing air compressor governor settings

Air brake systems must operate with air pressure within a prescribed range. The system's pressure range is controlled by the air compressor governor settings, which determine when the air compressor will cut-out and cut-in. Drivers can perform a test to determine the settings and to establish the normal operating pressure range for a particular vehicle.

The model year of a vehicle generally affects the governor pressure setting. Air brake system operating pressure ranges have increased over the past 20 years. Older systems may operate with lower pressure settings.

Air pressure gauges stop climbing with compressor cut-out. When a vehicle uses an air dryer, the exhaust cycle of the air dryer also indicates that the compressor has reached the cut-out setting. Observe the primary and secondary air tank gauges to confirm when the pressure stops climbing and when the cut-out setting has been reached.

The cut-in pressure setting is normally 138 to 173 kPa (20 to 25 psi) below the cut-out pressure setting. Compressor cut-in causes a change in the sound of the engine and can be observed when the air tank gauges begin to show an increase in pressure.

Cut-out pressure must be between 690 and 932 kPa (100 and 135 psi) and must never exceed 932 kPa (135 psi). Cut-in pressure must never be less than 552 kPa (80 psi).

When pressure settings are outside the prescribed range, the air brake system is defective.

Step-by-step procedure

1. Properly secure the vehicle and release the spring brakes.
2. Observe the primary and secondary air tank pressure gauges.
3. Run the engine until air brake system pressure reaches its maximum level and note the cut-out pressure setting.
4. Press and release the brake pedal several times to lower the system pressure and note the cut-in pressure setting.

Pass

✓ The vehicle passes the test when the cut-out pressure setting is between 690 and 932 kPa (100 and 135 psi) and the cut-in pressure setting is 552 kPa (80 psi) or higher.

Fail

✗ The vehicle fails the test when the cut-out pressure setting is higher than 932 kPa (135 psi) or lower than 690 kPa (100 psi), or cut-in pressure setting is lower than 552 kPa (80 psi).

Important: The Ontario Highway Traffic Act and regulations prohibit operation of a vehicle with air compressor governor settings outside the prescribed limits.

Testing system air loss rate

Drivers must be alert for air brake system leaks and pressure loss in the air tanks when brakes are not being used. These conditions indicate air loss in the air brake system. For safety, drivers should test the air loss rate of the vehicle's brake system.

To test the air loss rate of the brake system, release the spring brakes, establish normal air pressure and shut off the engine. Hold the brake pedal in the fully applied position and observe the air pressure readings for one minute.

The pressure will drop noticeably when the brakes are first applied but must not continue to drop at a rate greater than specified in the chart below. The amount of pressure drop that takes place when brakes are first applied is not considered when performing the air loss rate test. The air brake system is defective when air loss exceeds the specified values.

Air Loss Rates	
Type of vehicle	Maximum allowable air loss
Straight truck, tractor or bus	21 kPa (3 psi) per minute
Tractor and trailer	28 kPa (4 psi) per minute
Tractor and two or more trailers	41 kPa (6 psi) per minute

Step-by-step procedure

1. Properly secure the vehicle and release the spring brakes.
2. Ensure that the air brake system is within its normal operating pressure range. Shut off the engine.
3. Press and hold the brake pedal in the fully applied position.
4. Note the pressure indicated on the primary and secondary air tank gauges.
5. Note the change in pressure over one minute.

Pass

✓ The vehicle passes the test when the drop in pressure is equal to or less than the value specified for the vehicle.

Fail

✗ The vehicle fails the test when the drop in pressure exceeds the value specified for the vehicle.

Important: The Ontario Highway Traffic Act and regulations prohibit operation of a vehicle with an excessive air loss rate.

Testing a tractor (towing vehicle) protection valve

The tractor protection valve on a towing vehicle ensures that an air loss problem in the trailer does not result in loss of air from the towing vehicle.

To test the tractor protection valve, the trailer supply valve must be closed (pulled out), the trailer service line must be disconnected, and the service brakes applied. No air should be exhausting from the trailer service line. If air exhausts from the service line, the tractor protection valve is defective.

Step-by-step procedure

1. Ensure that the air brake system is within its normal operating pressure range.
2. Ensure the trailer supply valve is closed (pulled out).
3. Disconnect the trailer service air line coupler from either the trailer or the dead end coupler and place it where it can be observed.
4. Press and hold the brake pedal. (If there is a concern that the vehicle has no anti-compounding valve, ensure the vehicle is secure and release the spring brakes before applying service brakes.)
5. Observe whether air is exhausting from the trailer service line coupler.

Pass

✓ The vehicle passes the test if air does not exhaust from the trailer service line.

Fail

✗ The vehicle fails the test if air exhausts from the trailer service line.

Important: The Ontario Highway Traffic Act and regulations prohibit the operation of a vehicle with a defective tractor protection valve.

Testing the automatic application of the trailer spring brakes

A trailer's spring brakes must automatically apply whenever the trailer is disconnected from the towing vehicle. To test this, open (push in) the trailer supply valve to fully charge the trailer. Then pull out the trailer supply valve to close it. The trailer spring brakes should apply. Disconnecting the trailer air supply line also activates this function, but closing the trailer supply valve is the recommended testing method. Brake application may be confirmed by gently applying engine power to move the vehicle forward or backward.

If the trailer spring brakes fail to apply automatically when the trailer supply valve is closed, the trailer brakes are defective.

Step-by-step procedure

1. Ensure the trailer supply valve is open (pushed in) and the trailer is fully charged.
2. Ensure the air brake system is within its normal operating pressure range.
3. Pull out the trailer supply valve to close it.
4. Observe the trailer for application of the trailer's spring brakes.
5. If necessary, confirm brake application by attempting to gently move the vehicle forward or backward.

Pass

✓ The vehicle passes the test if the trailer spring brakes apply automatically.

Fail

✗ The vehicle fails the test if the trailer spring brakes do not apply.

Important: The Ontario Highway Traffic Act and regulations prohibit the operation of a vehicle with defective trailer spring brakes.

Testing the spring (parking and emergency) brakes

A vehicle's spring brakes must be capable of holding the vehicle in place. If the test is being conducted on a towing vehicle and trailer, select the vehicle on which to perform this test. It is preferable that this test be performed on the spring brakes of the towing vehicle. However, when a towing vehicle is pulling a trailer, it may not be possible to test its spring brakes separately. This can be done only on towing vehicle systems where the trailer can be supplied air while the parking brakes of the towing vehicle are released. Spring brakes can be tested by gently applying engine power in a low gear while the brakes are applied. The vehicle may rock slightly but the wheels should not turn during the test.

Failure of the spring brakes to hold the vehicle stationary indicates defective spring brakes.

Step-by-step procedure

1. Apply the spring brakes on the vehicle to be tested and remove wheel chocks.
2. Gently apply engine power in a low gear.
3. Observe the vehicle's response. The vehicle may rock and shake and the wheels may move slightly, but there should be no significant movement of the vehicle.

Pass

✓ The vehicle passes the test if the spring brakes hold the vehicle in place.

Fail

✗ The vehicle fails the test if the spring brakes do not hold the vehicle in place.

Important: The Ontario Highway Traffic Act and regulations prohibit the operation of a vehicle with defective spring brakes.

Testing the air tank drain valves

Air tanks must be drained regularly and the discharge observed for abnormalities. Some moisture may be discharged from the supply tank. A much smaller amount of moisture may be discharged from the remaining air tanks. A significant quantity of moisture being discharged from the supply tank — even when the tank is drained on a regular basis — may be normal. Discharge of a significant quantity of moisture from the remaining air tanks is not normal and should be reported.

While a small amount of oil may be found in the supply tank, any visible quantity of oil should be reported or repaired. When oil is found in any other air tank, there is risk of air brake system contamination and the condition must be reported.

When there is a sudden increase in the amount of moisture or oil drained from any tank, the condition must be reported and repaired. Any malfunctioning drain valve must be repaired.

The supply tank should always be drained first to prevent accumulated moisture in the supply tank passing further into the system. Drivers must know the location of all air tanks and drains.

It is important to note that the body design and suspension of some vehicles may limit safe access to the air tanks and drains unless the vehicle is supported on a hoist, or is over a pit or ramp.

Step-by-step procedure

1. Ensure that the air brake system is within its normal operating pressure range.
2. Locate and drain the supply tank until the valve discharges only clean air.
3. Locate and drain the remaining air tanks.
4. Watch the discharge from each air tank and ensure that all air tank drain valves function properly.

Pass

✓ The vehicle passes the test when each drain valve functions properly.

Fail

✗ The vehicle fails the test when any drain valve fails to function properly.

Important: The Ontario Highway Traffic Act and regulations prohibit the operation of a vehicle with defective air tank drain valves.

Key Points To Remember

- To test low air pressure warning devices, activate the device by reducing air pressure. If the device fails to activate or activates below 380 kPa (55 psi), the low air pressure warning device is defective.
- To test air pressure build-up time, lower air pressure to less than 552 kPa (80 psi), run the engine at 600 to 900 rpm and observe the time it takes for pressure to rise from 587 to 690 kPa (85 to 100 psi). If the air pressure build-up time is greater than two minutes, the air brake system is defective.
- Test air compressor governor settings by observing the compressor cut-in and cut-out settings. If cut-out pressure is greater than 932 kPa (135 psi) or less than 690 kPa (100 psi), or cut-in pressure is less than 552 kPa (80 psi), the air brake system is defective.
- Test air loss rate by checking for audible air leaks and then observe the air pressure gauges with full air pressure, the engine stopped, spring brakes released and service brakes applied. If the pressure drop in one minute exceeds the value specified for the vehicle, the air brake system is defective.
- Test the tractor protection valve by listening for air exhausting from the trailer service line with the trailer supply valve closed, the trailer service line disconnected and the service brakes applied. If air is exhausting from the trailer service line, the tractor protection valve is defective.
- Test the automatic application of the trailer spring brakes with the trailer supply valve open (pushed in) and the system fully charged. Pull out the trailer supply valve to close it and listen for the trailer spring brakes to apply automatically. If the brakes do not apply automatically, the trailer spring brakes are defective.
- To test the effectiveness of the spring brakes, gently apply engine power with the spring brakes applied. If the spring brakes fail to hold the vehicle stationary, the spring brakes are defective.
- To test the air tank drain valves, drain each air tank while observing the discharge. If any drain valve fails to work properly or has an abnormal discharge of moisture or oil, the air brake system is defective.

Chapter 11

Proper brake adjustment is important to your safety and the safety of other road users. Drivers of vehicles with air brakes must inspect brake adjustment regularly using a reliable inspection method. This chapter explains how to carry out such an inspection.

Brake adjustment must be inspected regularly

The pushrod stroke of each brake chamber is critical to the proper function of a brake system. As the brakes wear, brake pushrod stroke increases. Brake wear occurs at varying rates, depending on the type of vehicle and driving conditions. To determine whether brake adjustment is correct, the pushrod stroke must be inspected at least daily. When brake pushrod stroke exceeds the adjustment limit, the brake is out of adjustment.

Brake pushrod stroke must comply with the Ontario Highway Traffic Act and regulations. Each air brake chamber's pushrod stroke must not exceed the specified adjustment limits.

Since adjustment limits vary depending on the size and type of air brake chamber, you must be able to identify the particular brake chamber in use. Brake chamber size can be determined by measuring the diameter of the clamp used to hold the brake chamber together or by locating the size markings on the brake chamber.

The most common brake chamber size is 30. However, there are vehicles using both smaller and larger sizes. For example, sizes 16, 20, 24 and 36 brake chambers may be used.

Measuring the diameter of brake chambers requires a special tool. Locating and reading

the size markings on a brake chamber may require removing dirt, corrosion and paint from the brake chamber surfaces.

You are most likely to determine the size of the brake chambers on any vehicle through your employer or the vehicle owner's manual. This will avoid the need to measure a brake chamber or locate size markings. The type of brake chamber also affects the specified brake adjustment limit, which can vary by 19 millimetres or more between standard and long-stroke brake chambers. Long-stroke brake chambers can be identified by three visible characteristics:

- The air lines attach to a square port in the brake chamber body.
- A trapezoidal tag is placed under the clamp bolt that indicates the brake chamber's maximum stroke dimension. (Not the brake adjustment limit.)

- Markings are placed on the brake chamber body to indicate that it is a long-stroke brake chamber and only long-stroke diaphragms are to be used as replacements.

The most visible and permanent of the markings used to identify long-stroke brake chambers are the square ports. Standard brake chambers have round ports.

It is critical to use correct inspection methods to obtain reliable inspection results. The most reliable method for inspecting brake adjustment is to measure the applied pushrod stroke.

Step-by-step procedure for measuring applied pushrod stroke

It is important to note that the body design and suspension of some vehicles may limit safe access to certain brake components unless the vehicle is supported on a hoist or is over a pit or ramp. Also, some brake

systems have covers or housings that conceal the brake linkage, making it impossible to inspect brake adjustment using the techniques described here.

1. Secure the vehicle with wheel chocks or blocks.
2. Ensure air pressure is above 621 kPa (90 psi) and release the spring brakes.
3. Select one of the following methods:
   - **Method 1:** Mark the pushrod at the brake chamber or at a suitable fixed reference point. (Use chalk, soapstone, marker or other similar instrument — marks must be narrow and precise.)
   - **Method 2:** Measure the released position of the pushrod. (Measure and note the distance from a point on the pushrod to a suitable fixed point at the brake chamber. This is measurement number 1.)

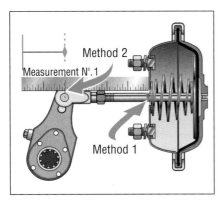

Diagram 11-1: Air pressure above 621 kPa (90 psi) with spring brakes released.

4. Raise or lower the air pressure by running the engine or pumping the brake pedal until both the primary and secondary air tank gauges display 621 to 690 kPa (90 to 100 psi).

5. Shut off the engine.

6. Press and hold the brake pedal in the fully applied position.

7. Determine the applied pushrod stroke. (Continue to use the previously selected method).
  - **Method 1:** Measure the distance from the brake chamber or fixed reference point to the mark on the pushrod.
  - **Method 2:** Measure the applied position of the pushrod. (Remeasure and note the distance from the previously selected point on the pushrod to the previously selected fixed point at the brake chamber. This is measurement number 2.) Subtract measurement 1 from measurement 2 to calculate the applied pushrod stroke measurement.

8. Determine the number size (such as 16, 20, 24 or 30) and type (such as standard or long-stroke) of the brake chamber.

9. Determine the adjustment limit for the brake chamber. (See the chart on page 85.)

10. Compare the applied pushrod stroke to the applicable adjustment limit and identify any brake that exceeds the adjustment limit as defective.

Note: All drivers are required to demonstrate an applied pushrod stroke measurement method for inspecting brake adjustment as part of the Ministry of Transportation air brake endorsement practical examination.

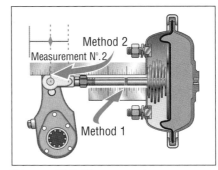

Diagram 11-2: Air pressure between 621 and 690 kPa (90 and 100 psi) with the service brake fully applied.

Brake stroke indicators

Brake chamber pushrods are generally marked with some type of indicator that becomes visible when pushrod stroke exceeds the adjustment limit. Brake stroke indicators can also be fitted to the brake linkage, which include external reference points to provide a visual indication of the applied pushrod stroke.

Pushrod stroke indicators must be correctly installed and maintained, and drivers must be fully trained in the proper use of brake stroke indicators to ensure reliable brake adjustment inspection results are obtained.

Automatic slack or brake adjusters

Automatic slack or brake adjusters are used to avoid the need to regularly perform manual brake re-adjustment. When they are properly installed and maintained, automatic slack adjusters are very reliable.

Inspection of brake adjustment must be carried out whether automatic or manual slack adjusters are used.

Re-adjusting brakes

When brakes with manual slack adjusters are out of adjustment, they must be re-adjusted so that the pushrod stroke is less than the adjustment limit. Only certified technicians may repair and perform brake re-adjustments on manual slack adjusters. In Ontario, drivers can become certified to perform brake re-adjustments on manual slack adjusters. Only those who have obtained certification are permitted to perform brake re-adjustments. This certification does not permit you to manually re-adjust automatic slack adjusters.

Automatic slack adjusters, if they are working properly, do not require regular re-adjustment. If periodic re-adjustments are required it means that the automatic slack adjuster is defective and must be repaired by a certified technician. Only certified technicians are permitted to perform re-adjustments or repairs on automatic slack adjustors. It is dangerous for someone who is not certified to attempt to adjust the automatic slack adjustors. You may unknowingly damage the brake and cause it to malfunction. Check your automatic slack adjusters often to ensure that the adjustments are correct; however, do not attempt to repair them yourself.

Important: The Ontario Highway Traffic Act and regulations prohibit the operation of a vehicle with a brake that is out of adjustment.

Key Points To Remember

- Measuring applied pushrod stroke is a reliable method for inspecting brake adjustment.
- Inspection of brake adjustment at each wheel should be performed with air pressure between 621 and 690 kPa (90 and 100 psi), the engine shut off and service brakes fully applied.
- When pushrod stroke exceeds the adjustment limit of the brake chamber the brake is out of adjustment.

- Only qualified individuals may repair or re-adjust brakes.
- Drivers who have a valid Ontario air brake adjustment certificate are qualified to re-adjust the brakes on vehicles fitted with manual slack adjusters.
- The Ontario Highway Traffic Act and regulations prohibit the operation of a vehicle with a brake that is out of adjustment.

Chapter 12

This chapter includes inspection checklists, charts and circuit diagrams that will help you to complete the inspections you need to make, as well as help you to prepare for the Ministry of Transportation air brake endorsement practical examination.

Items to Bring to Practical Examination

Drivers completing a practical test must come to the test equipped with the following items:

1. Wheel chocks or blocks
2. A stopwatch or a watch with a second hand
3. Awareness of the size and type of all brake chambers on the vehicle in which they are being tested
4. A means of holding the brake pedal in the applied position
5. A means of marking the pushrod*
6. A device for measuring pushrod stroke*
7. A chart of brake adjustment limits (optional)
8. Protective headgear*
9. Protective eyewear*

does not apply to motor coaches

Mechanical inspection checklist

Use this checklist as a guide when completing a mechanical inspection of the air brake system components.

Note: When performing an inspection as part of a practical examination, tell the examiner what you are testing at each step of the inspection.

Prepare the vehicle for inspection:
- Apply the spring brakes.
- Put wheel chocks or blocks in place.

Inspect foundation brake components at each wheel for:
- brake shoe lining not contacting the brake drum;
- damaged, missing or malfunctioning foundation brake components; and
- cracked, loose, missing or contaminated brake lining, improper drum contact or lining thickness that is less than required.

Inspect brake chambers at each wheel for:
- audible air leaks;
- cracks and non-manufactured holes;
- mismatched air brake chamber size on a steering axle; and
- mismatched slack adjuster length on a steering axle.

Inspect brake drums or rotors at each wheel for:
- cracked or broken brake drum or rotor.

Inspect all accessible air lines for:
- audible air leak;
- damaged or worn air line; and
- improper fittings used to connect or repair an air line.

Inspect air tanks for:
- insecure mounting.

Inspect air compressors for:
- loose air compressor drive belt pulley;
- loose, cut or frayed air compressor drive belt; and
- insecure air compressor mounting, bracket or fastener.

Functional inspection checklist

Use this checklist as a guide when completing an inspection of air brake system operation.

Note: When performing this inspection as part of a practical examination, indicate to the examiner what you are testing at the beginning of each segment.

Prepare the vehicle for inspection:
- Apply the spring brakes.
- Put wheel chocks or blocks in place.

Test low air warning device
- Ensure air pressure is at least 621 kPa (90 psi). (If air pressure is too low, warning will activate as soon as ignition key is turned on.)
- Ensure key is 'on'. Engine may be running or shut off. (If ignition key is not turned on the warning will not activate.)

- Press and release the brake pedal several times until the low air warning device activates.
- Watch the pressure gauges and note the pressure value when the low air warning device activates. (Warning may be only a light or a light and an audible device.)

If the device fails to activate or activates below 380 kPa (55 psi), the vehicle is defective.

Test air pressure build-up time
- If the vehicle has a trailer attached, ensure the trailer supply valve is closed (pulled out).
- Reduce air pressure to below 552 kPa (80 psi).
- Maintain engine speed of 600 to 900 rpm.
- Observe time for pressure to rise from 587 to 690 kPa (85 to 100 psi) while maintaining specified engine speed.

If the air pressure build-up time is greater than two minutes, the vehicle is defective.

Report defective vehicle conditions
Drivers are required to report defective vehicle conditions.

It is illegal to operate or drive a defective vehicle.

Test air compressor governor settings
- Observe the air pressure gauges until pressure ceases climbing. (Air dryer purge also signals compressor cut-out.)
- Reduce air pressure slowly and note the point where pressure begins to climb again. (A change in the sound of the air compressor also signals compressor cut-in.)

If cut-out pressure is greater than 932 kPa (135 psi) or is less than 690 kPa (100 psi) and/or cut-in pressure is less than 552 kPa (80 psi) the vehicle is defective.

Test air loss rate
- Ensure vehicle is secure and release the spring brakes.
- Ensure air system pressure is between cut-in and cut-out settings and shut off the engine.
- Press and hold the brake pedal in the fully applied position.
- Observe the air pressure gauges for one minute and note any change in air pressure. (Disregard the initial pressure drop and begin test after pressure has stabilized.)

If the pressure drop exceeds the value specified for the vehicle, the vehicle is defective.

Test tractor (towing vehicle) protection valve
- Ensure air pressure is within its normal operating range.
- Ensure the trailer supply valve is closed (pulled out).
- Remove the trailer service line coupler from the trailer or its

storage location and place it where it can be observed.
- Press and hold the brake pedal. (Note: If concerned that the vehicle has no anti-compounding valve, ensure the vehicle is secure and release the spring brakes before applying service brakes.)
- Note whether air exhausts from the trailer service line coupler.

If air exhausts from the trailer service line, the vehicle is defective.

Test automatic application of the trailer spring brakes
- Ensure trailer supply valve is open (pushed in), air pressure is in the normal operating range and trailer is fully charged.
- Close (pull out) the trailer supply valve. (Note: The trailer supply line may also be disconnected but this practice is not recommended while the line is under pressure.)
- Air should be heard exhausting

from the trailer spring brakes. (Note: If uncertain that the trailer spring brakes have applied, gently apply engine power to confirm brake application.)

If the trailer spring brakes do not apply, the vehicle is defective.

Test spring (parking/emergency) brakes
- Apply the spring brakes.
- Remove wheel chocks or blocks.
- Apply engine power gently to the wheels and observe the vehicle response.

If the spring brakes fail to hold the vehicle stationary, the vehicle is defective.

Inspect air tank drain valves
- Ensure air system pressure is within its normal operating range.
- Drain the supply tank until it discharges only clean air.
- Drain the remaining air tanks.

- Watch the discharge from the air tanks and ensure that the drain valves function properly.

If any drain valve fails to function properly, the vehicle is defective.

Report defective vehicle conditions.
Drivers are required to report defective vehicle conditions. It is illegal to operate or drive a defective vehicle.

Brake adjustment inspection checklist
Use this checklist as a guide when inspecting brake adjustment.

Note: If you are performing this inspection as part of a practical examination, you must know your vehicle's brake chamber size and type and bring the following items:
- a means of applying the service brakes;
- a means of measuring the applied pushrod stroke;
- a means of marking the pushrod if this method will be used; and
- a chart of adjustment limits (see page 85).

Inspect brake adjustment
Ensure air pressure is above 621 kPa (90 psi).
- Release spring brakes.
- Select one of the following methods and indicate which method will be used:
  Method 1: Mark the pushrod at the brake chamber or a suitable fixed reference point. (Use chalk, soapstone, marker or other similar instrument. Pushrod marks must be narrow and precise.)
  Method 2: Measure and note the released position of the pushrod. (Measure the distance from a point on the pushrod to a suitable fixed point at the brake chamber. This is measurement number 1.)
- Raise or lower air pressure by running the engine or pumping the brake pedal until both the primary and secondary air tank pressure gauges display 621 to 690 kPa (90 to 100 psi).
- Press the brake pedal and use a suitable means to hold the brakes fully applied in order to leave the vehicle and inspect the pushrod stroke.

- Determine the applied pushrod stroke. (Continue to use the previously selected method.)
  Method 1: Measure the distance from the brake chamber or the fixed reference point to the mark on the pushrod.
  Method 2: Measure the applied position of the pushrod. (Re-measure and note the distance from the previously selected point on the pushrod to the previously selected fixed point at the brake chamber. This is measurement number 2.) Subtract measurement number 1 from measurement number 2 to calculate the applied pushrod stroke measurement.
- Identify the brake chamber size. (16, 20, 24, 30, for example.)
- Identify the brake chamber type. (Standard, long-stroke, for example.)
- Identify the adjustment limit of the brake chamber. (This step may involve referring to a chart or table. See chart on page 85.)
- Repeat the above steps at each wheel.

If any brake pushrod stroke exceeds the adjustment limit, the vehicle is defective.

Air Supply Subsystem Circuit Diagram

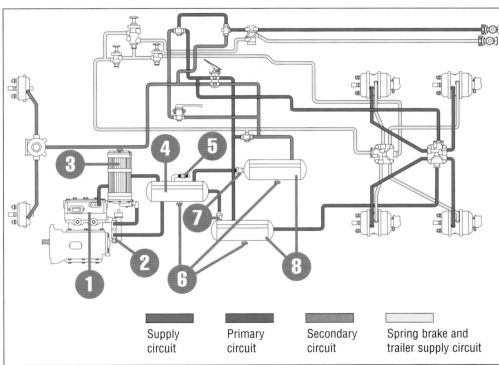

1. Air compressor
2. Governor
3. Air dryer
4. Supply (wet) tank
5. Safety valve
6. Air tank drain valves
7. One-way check valves
8. Primary and secondary (dry) tanks

Note: This is only a sample circuit diagram. Components and their positions may be different on your vehicle.1-3/4

Supply circuit
Primary circuit
Secondary circuit
Spring brake and trailer supply circuit

Diagram 12-1

Coach or Bus Brake Subsystem Circuit Diagram

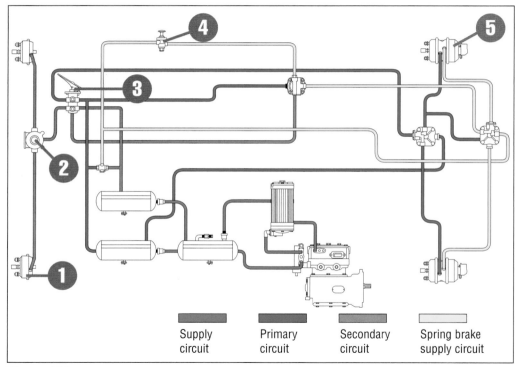

1. Service brake chambers
2. Front wheel-limiting valve
3. Brake pedal
4. Spring brake control valve
5. Spring brake chambers

Note: This is only a sample circuit diagram. Components and their positions may be different on your vehicle.

Supply circuit

Primary circuit

Secondary circuit

Spring brake supply circuit

Diagram 12-2

Towing Vehicle Brake Subsystem Circuit Diagram

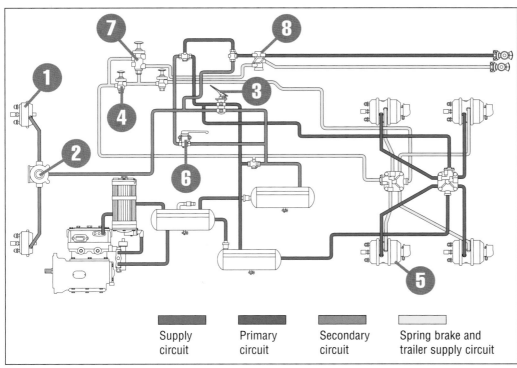

1. Service brake chambers
2. Front wheel-limiting valve
3. Brake pedal
4. Spring brake control valve
5. Spring brake chambers
6. Hand valve
7. Trailer supply valve
8. Tractor protection valve

Note: This is only a sample circuit diagram. Components and their positions may be different on your vehicle.

Supply circuit Primary circuit Secondary circuit Spring brake and trailer supply circuit

Diagram 12-3

83

Trailer Brake Subsystem Circuit Diagram

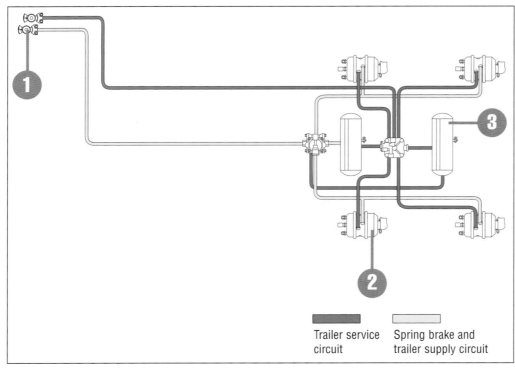

1. Trailer couplers (gladhands)
2. Spring brake chambers
3. Air tanks

Note: This is only a sample circuit diagram. Components and their positions may be different on your vehicle.

Trailer service circuit

Spring brake and trailer supply circuit

Diagram 12-4

Brake Adjustment Limits — Clamp-type Chambers

Size	Marking	Outside Diameter		Adjustment Limit	
6	None	4-1/2"	(115mm)	1-1/4"	(32mm)
9	None	5-1/4"	(133mm)	1-3/8"	(35mm)
12	None	5-11/16"	(144mm)	1-3/8"	(35mm)
16	None	6-3/8"	(162mm)	1-3/4"	(45mm)
16 L	L Stamped In Cover, Stroke Tag	6-3/8"	(162mm)	2"	(51mm)
20	None	6-25/32"	(172mm)	1-3/4"	(45mm)
20 L	L Stamped In Cover, Stroke Tag	6-25/32"	(172mm)	2"	(51mm)
24	None	7-7/32"	(183mm)	1-3/4"	(45mm)
24 L	L Stamped In Cover, Stroke Tag	7-7/32"	(183mm)	2"	(51mm)
24 LS	Square Ports, Tag & Cover Marking	7-7/32"	(183mm)	2-1/2"	(64mm)
30	None	8-3/32"	(205mm)	2"	(51mm)
30	DD3 (Bus/Coach)	8-1/8"	(206mm)	2-1/4"	(57mm)
30 LS	Square Ports, Tag & Cover Marking	8-3/32"	(205mm)	2-1/2"	(64mm)
36	None	9"	(228mm)	2-1/4"	(57mm)

Note: L denotes the long-stroke pushrod design.
Note: LS denotes the long-stroke pushrod design with square ports.

Conversion Charts: Air Pressure — Metric and Imperial Units

kPa to psi				psi to kPa			
kPa	psi	kPa	psi	psi	kPa	psi	kPa
5	3/4	300	43	1	7	55	380
10	1-1/2	350	51	2	14	60	414
15	2-1/4	400	58	3	21	65	449
20	3	450	65	4	28	70	483
25	3-1/2	500	72	5	35	75	518
30	4-1/4	550	80	6	41	80	552
35	5	600	87	7	48	85	587
40	5-3/4	650	94	8	55	90	621
45	6-1/2	700	101	9	62	95	655
50	7-1/4	750	109	10	69	100	690
60	8-3/4	800	116	15	103	105	725
70	10	850	123	20	138	110	759
80	11-1/2	900	130	25	173	115	794
90	13	950	138	30	207	120	828
100	14-1/2	1000	145	35	242	125	863
150	22	1050	152	40	276	130	897
200	29	1100	159	45	311	135	932
250	36			50	345	150	1035

Conversion chart

Imperial to Metric Converter

From	To	Multiply By
inches	centimetres	2.54
miles	kilometres	1.61
feet	metres	0.31
pounds	kilograms	0.46
miles per hour	kilometres per hour	1.61

Metric to Imperial Converter

From	To	Multiply By
centrimetres	inches	0.39
kilometres	miles	0.62
metres	feet	3.28
kilograms	pounds	2.21
kilometres per hour	miles per hour	0.61

Personalize your licence plates — with two to eight characters, as well as a great choice of colour graphics. Then you'll really stand out from the crowd.

Turn the page to find out more.

NOW THERE ARE MORE WAYS THAN EVER TO EXPRESS YOURSELF!

WE'RE HELPING YOU BUILD CHARACTERS.

Now you've got extra choices when creating your personalized licence plate. We've introduced seven and eight characters. So you've got even more to work with — a minimum of two characters and right up to eight. Just think of the possibilities.

Every personalized plate is one of a kind. No one else can have the same plate as yours.

For more information and to order your personalized plates, call 1-800-AUTO-PL8 (1-800-288-6758).

Or visit the ServiceOntario website: www.serviceontario.ca
Or drop by your local Driver and Vehicle Licence Issuing Office
Or one of 70 ServiceOntario kiosks.

Gift certificates are available too.

ONTARIO
BCRE8TVE
YOURS TO DISCOVER

ONTARIO
NOWYOURS
YOURS TO DISCOVER

Graphic licence plates are a hit! And now there are more than 40 choices available. Support your favourite Ontario sports team, community or arts organization, professional group or university. Or select a timeless icon like the loon or trillium.

For a totally unique look, add a colour graphic to a personalized plate with up to six characters.

So express yourself — with colour graphics and personalized licence plates.

For more information and to order your plates, call 1-800-AUTO-PL8 (1-800-288-6758).

Or visit our website: www.mto.gov.on.ca
Or drop by your local Driver and
Vehicle Licence Issuing Office
Or one of 70 ServiceOntario kiosks.

Gift certificates
are available too.

ADD SOME COLOUR WHERE IT COUNTS.

Other MTO Publications for you

Copies of this handbook and others may be
purchased from a:

- Retail store near you;
- DriveTest Centre;
- Driver and Vehicle Licence Issuing Office; or
- By calling (416) 326-5300 or 1-800-668-9938 (toll free)
- www.serviceontario.ca/publications

Prepayment required by cheque or credit card – VISA or Mastercard.
You may also pay with a certified cheque at DriveTest Centres.

Handbook prices are subject to 5% H.S.T and 5% shipping costs. The road map is subject to 13% H.S.T.,
and 5% shipping costs.

The Official Driver's Handbook

The Official Motorcycle Handbook

The Official Truck Handbook

The Official Bus Handbook

The Official Air Brake Handbook

The Official Ontario Road Map